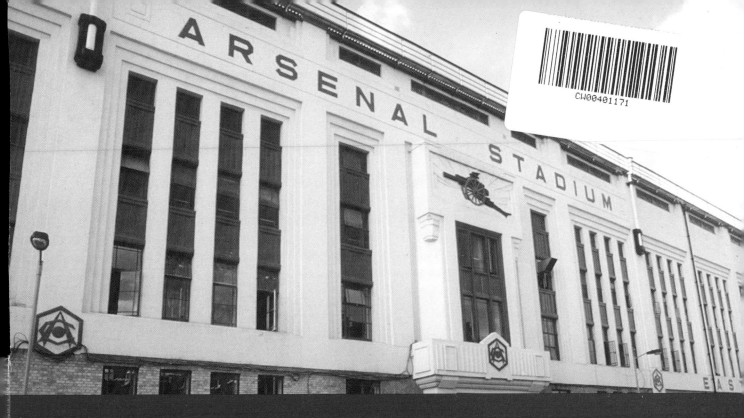

THE OFFICIAL
ARSENAL FC
Maths Book 3
Paul Broadbent

Gunning for Goals

Education is essential to everyone and basic skills such as English and Maths are vitally important to every child's development.

Teaching core subjects through sport, I feel, is the best way. Encouraging youngsters to reach their goals in the classroom through Arsenal based activities is both a motivational and rewarding exercise.

That's why the Club already spearheads a number of successful education initiatives, including after school learning programmes at the Arsenal Study Support Centre and through the Arsenal 'Double Club'.

The inception of the Official Arsenal FC Workbook series further illustrates the Club's commitment to education. More importantly these books present an interesting and fun approach to learning at home.

I hope this book motivates you to accomplish your goals.

Arsène Wenger

Arsenal Study Support Centre
28 Carleton Road
London N7 0EQ
stevewilson@arsenalstudysupport.org
Telephone 020 7697 8467
Fax 020 7697 0873

Arsenal Double Club
Arsenal Stadium
London N5 1BU
bnicholas@arsenal.co.uk
Telephone 020 7704 4140
Fax 020 7704 4101

Kick-off

The Arsenal FC books are a fun way to learn and practise your Maths skills. Each book contains: Theme visits to Arsenal FC, six Big Matches and a board game!

The 'theme' visits

Learn more about Arsenal FC and football.

Enjoy the fun activities (*answers on pages 30–31*).

The Big Matches

Learn a new skill.

Practise the skill.

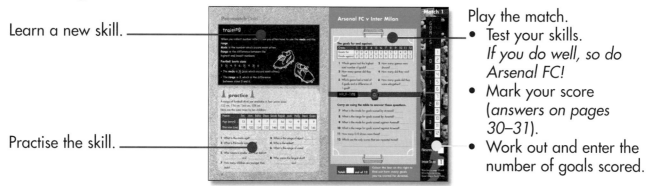

Play the match.
- Test your skills. *If you do well, so do Arsenal FC!*
- Mark your score (*answers on pages 30–31*).
- Work out and enter the number of goals scored.

After the match:
Enter each result on page 28. Work out Arsenal FC's league position!

The board game

What you need.

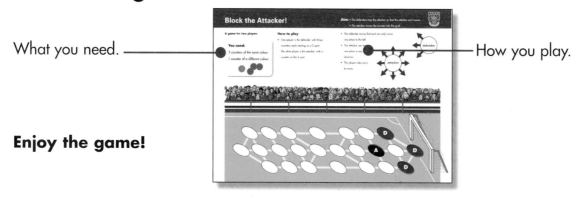

How you play.

Enjoy the game!

Contents

The Stadium

Highbury can hold 38 500 spectators, which is not enough for all of the club's supporters. That is why they plan to build a bigger stadium within the next five years. In the days when Highbury still had terraces, its biggest attendance was 73 295 against Sunderland in March 1935.

Here are the attendance figures for four Arsenal matches.

2 Complete this place-value table.

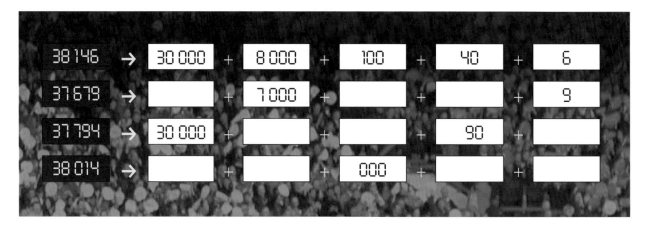

38 146	→	30 000	+	8 000	+	100	+	40	+	6
37 679	→		+	7 000	+		+		+	9
37 794	→	30 000	+		+		+	90	+	
38 014	→		+		+	000	+		+	

Did you know ... ?
Arsenal's proposed new stadium will be custom-built and should hold up to about 60 000 spectators. The club has outgrown Highbury, and people have not been able to get in to see their favourite team play.

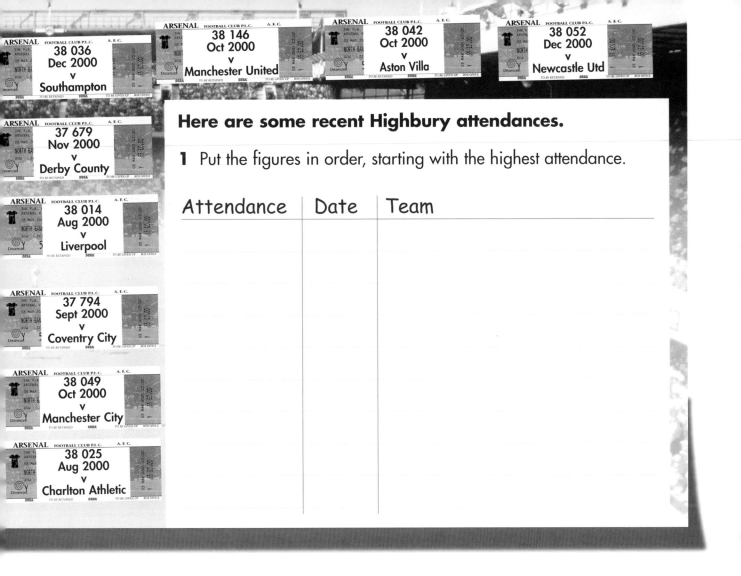

ARSENAL FOOTBALL CLUB P.L.C.   A. F. C.
38 036
Dec 2000
v
Southampton

ARSENAL FOOTBALL CLUB P.L.C.   A. F. C.
38 146
Oct 2000
v
Manchester United

ARSENAL FOOTBALL CLUB P.L.C.   A. F. C.
38 042
Oct 2000
v
Aston Villa

ARSENAL FOOTBALL CLUB P.L.C.   A. F. C.
38 052
Dec 2000
v
Newcastle Utd

ARSENAL FOOTBALL CLUB P.L.C.   A. F. C.
37 679
Nov 2000
v
Derby County

ARSENAL FOOTBALL CLUB P.L.C.   A. F. C.
38 014
Aug 2000
v
Liverpool

ARSENAL FOOTBALL CLUB P.L.C.   A. F. C.
37 794
Sept 2000
v
Coventry City

ARSENAL FOOTBALL CLUB P.L.C.   A. F. C.
38 049
Oct 2000
v
Manchester City

ARSENAL FOOTBALL CLUB P.L.C.   A. F. C.
38 025
Aug 2000
v
Charlton Athletic

Here are some recent Highbury attendances.

1 Put the figures in order, starting with the highest attendance.

Attendance	Date	Team

3 Make ten four-digit numbers out of 73 295. An example could be 2395.

Write them in order, starting with the largest.

_____

_____

_____

_____

_____

_____

_____

Did you know ... ?
**Arsenal moved to Highbury in 1913.
It was too close for comfort for their
new north London neighbours
Tottenham Hotspur, and they have
been fierce rivals ever since.**

5

training

When you collect number information you often have to use the **mode** and the **range**.

Mode is the number which occurs most often.

Range is the difference between the highest and lowest numbers.

Football boots sizes

3 $3\frac{1}{2}$ 4 5 6 $3\frac{1}{2}$ 4 $3\frac{1}{2}$ 6

- The **mode** is $3\frac{1}{2}$ (size which occurs most often).

- The **range** is 3, which is the difference between sizes 3 and 6.

practice

A range of football shirts are available in four junior sizes:
122 cm, 134 cm, 146 cm, 158 cm.

Here are the sizes worn by ten children:

Name	Jon	Ann	Balvir	Dave	Sarah	Rajesh	Jack	Holly	Demi	Ewan
Age (years)	13	8	9	7	11	14	10	9	8	9
Shirt size (cm)	158	122	134	122	146	158	146	146	134	146

1 What is the mode age? _____

2 What is the range of ages? _____

3 What is the mode size of shirt?

_____

4 Who is the eldest? _____

6 What is the range of sizes?

_____

5 Who wears a smaller shirt than Balvir?

_____ and _____

8 Who wears the largest shirt?

_____ and _____

7 How many children are younger than Jack? _____

Arsenal FC v Inter Milan

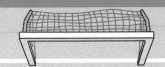

The goals for and against.

Game	1	2	3	4	5	6	7	8	9	10	11	12
Goals for	2	0	4	2	0	2	3	5	1	4	0	3
Goals against	2	0	1	0	3	0	0	1	1	1	0	2

1 Which game had the highest total number of goals? _____

2 How many games were drawn? _____

3 How many games did they lose? _____

4 How many did they win? _____

5 Which game had a total of 5 goals and a difference of 1 goal? _____

6 How many goals did they score altogether? _____

HALF-TIME

Carry on using the table to answer these questions.

7 What is the mode for goals scored by Arsenal? _____

8 What is the range for goals scored by Arsenal? _____

9 What is the mode for goals scored against Arsenal? _____

10 What is the range for goals scored against Arsenal? _____

11 How many 0–0 draws were there? _____

12 Which are the only scores that are repeated twice?

_____

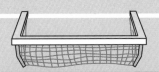

Total: ☐ **out of 12**

Colour the bar on the right to find out how many goals you've scored for Arsenal.

GOALS

0	1
	2
	3
1	4
	5
	6
2	7
	8
	9
3	10
	11
4	12

ARSENAL FC ☐

INTER MILAN **1**

Now turn to page 28 and fill in the score on the Super-League Results Table.

The 1970s

The decade started brilliantly for Arsenal, when they won their first double – the championship and the FA Cup – in their history. It ended a long drought for the club, as it had been 18 years since they were champions and 21 years since they held the FA Cup.

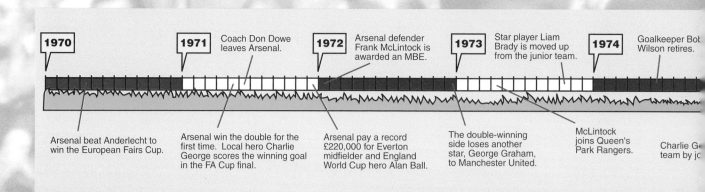

1970

1971 Coach Don Dowe leaves Arsenal.

1972 Arsenal defender Frank McLintock is awarded an MBE.

1973 Star player Liam Brady is moved up from the junior team.

1974 Goalkeeper Bob Wilson retires.

Arsenal beat Anderlecht to win the European Fairs Cup.

Arsenal win the double for the first time. Local hero Charlie George scores the winning goal in the FA Cup final.

Arsenal pay a record £220,000 for Everton midfielder and England World Cup hero Alan Ball.

The double-winning side loses another star, George Graham, to Manchester United.

McLintock joins Queen's Park Rangers.

Charlie G team by jo

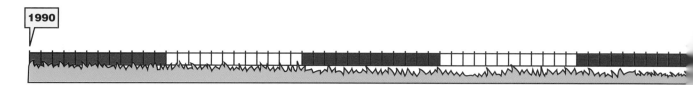

1990

A football timeline from 1990 to 2000.

6 Put some information about yourself and your love of football on the timeline above.

- The best football matches you have played in.
- The best football matches you have seen.
- When you were born.

- When you started school.
- The most goals you have scored.

Use the timeline to answer these questions.

1 Which month and year did Arsenal win their first league

double? _____

2 What year and month did Bob Wilson retire in? _____

3 Who scored the winning goal in the 1971 FA Cup final? _____

4 How many FA Cups did Arsenal win in the 1970s? _____

5 Which European trophy did the team win in the 1970s? _____

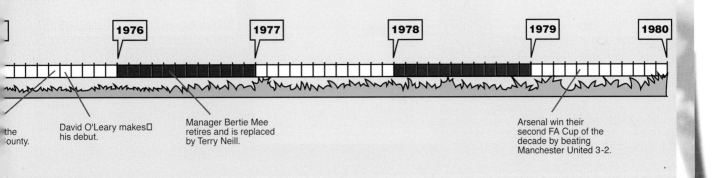

| 1976 | 1977 | 1978 | 1979 | 1980 |

the
:ounty.

David O'Leary makes□
his debut.

Manager Bertie Mee
retires and is replaced
by Terry Neill.

Arsenal win their
second FA Cup of the
decade by beating
Manchester United 3-2.

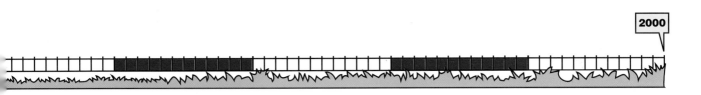

| 2000 |

EXTRA TIME

Knuckle months

This is a way to remember how many days are in each month.

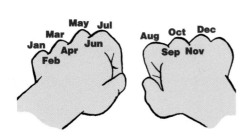

May Jul
Mar
Jan Jun
  Apr
  Feb

Aug Oct Dec
  Sep Nov

All the 'knuckle months' have 31 days.

February has 28 days. April, June, September

and November have 30 days.

7 How many days are in July? _____

8 How many days are in December? _____

training

The **area** of a rectangle = **length** × **breadth**.

The **perimeter** is the total distance around the edge.

5 cm

Area = 5 cm × 4 cm

= 20 cm^2

4 cm

5 cm

Perimeter

4 cm $= 5 + 4 + 5 + 4$ cm

$= 18$ cm

Some shapes can be broken into rectangles.

practice

A Calculate the area and the perimeter of each of these.

1 20 m

8 m

perimeter = _____

area = _____

2 6 m

4 m

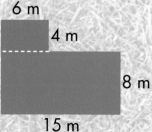

8 m

15 m

perimeter = _____

area = _____

3 3 m

3 m

3 m

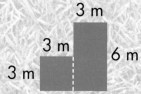

6 m

perimeter = _____

area = _____

B 1 The perimeter of a square is 32 cm. What is the area?

_____ cm^2

2 The area of a square is 49 cm^2. What is the perimeter?

_____ cm

Arsenal FC v St Etienne

Calculate the areas of these shapes.

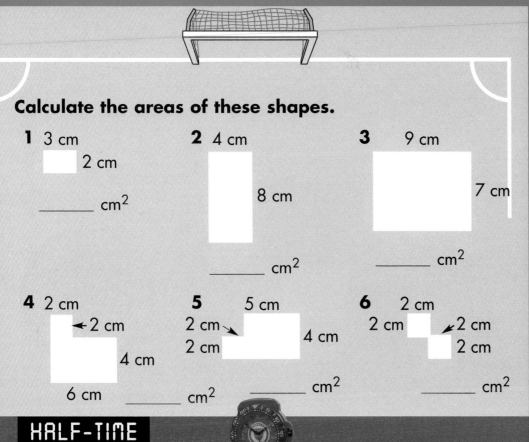

1 3 cm
2 cm

_____ cm²

2 4 cm
8 cm

_____ cm²

3 9 cm
7 cm

_____ cm²

4 2 cm
←2 cm
4 cm
6 cm _____ cm²

5 5 cm
2 cm→
2 cm
4 cm

_____ cm²

6 2 cm
2 cm ←2 cm
2 cm

_____ cm²

HALF-TIME

Calculate the perimeters of these shapes.

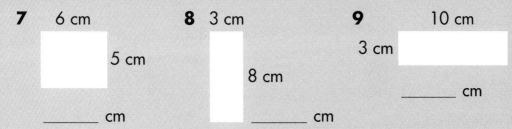

7 6 cm
5 cm

_____ cm

8 3 cm
8 cm

_____ cm

9 10 cm
3 cm

_____ cm

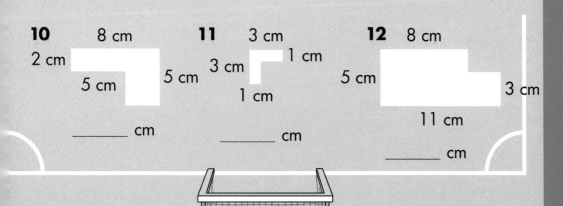

10 8 cm
2 cm
5 cm   5 cm

_____ cm

11 3 cm
3 cm   1 cm
1 cm

_____ cm

12 8 cm
5 cm
3 cm
11 cm

_____ cm

Total: _____ out of 12

Colour the bar on the right to find out how many goals you've scored for Arsenal.

ARSENAL FC [ ]

ST ETIENNE **1**

Now turn to page 28 and fill in the score on the Super-League Results Table.

The Arsenal FC Shop

Arsenal's shop at Highbury attracts thousands of customers and has a huge range of products that come with the Arsenal logo.

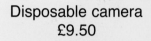
Disposable camera
£9.50

Lunch box
£6.50

Mini football
£5.00

Wallet
£4.25

Wall clock
£9.99

The above prices are examples for this exercise and may not correspond to Shop prices.

Shopping in the official Arsenal FC Shop.

1 Each shopper has £30 to spend. They each buy three items.

Work out the total cost and the change given for each shopper.

a	b	c
Wallet	Mug	Lunch box
Camera	Clock	Shin pads
Football	Baseball cap	Key ring
Total	**Total**	**Total**
Change	**Change**	**Change**

2 What is the total cost of four wallets? _____

3 Rajesh has £25 to spend. If he buys a camera and a clock, has he enough money left for a mug? _____

4 Which costs more – three mugs or five key rings? _____

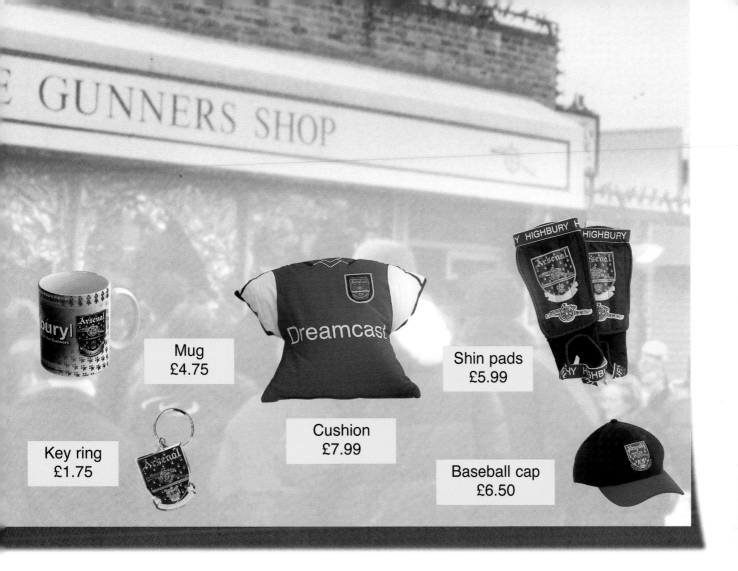

5 Which items would **you** choose? The total cost must be less than £30.

_____

6 Kim wants to send a clock in the post, as a present for a friend.

The postage costs £1.55. She has four 35p stamps and three 25p stamps.

a Which stamps will she use to make this total?

_____

b Which different amounts could you stick on a

parcel with these stamps?

_____

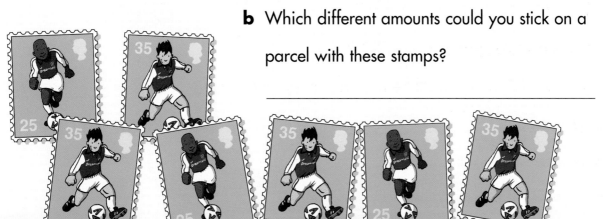

training

One number is **divisible** by another number if there is **no** remainder.

27 is divisible by 3 and 9 (27 ÷ 3 = 9, 27 ÷ 9 = 3)

All whole numbers obey these rules.

• All even numbers are divisible by 2.

• When the last two digits are divisible by 4, the whole number is divisible by 4.

• When the last digit is 5 or 0, the whole number is divisible by 5.

• When the last digit is 0, the whole number is divisible by 10.

• When the digits total 9, the whole number is divisible by 9.

practice

A Write the numbers in the correct places on these Venn diagrams.

Divisible by 5	Divisible by 2

Divisible by 9	Divisible by 10

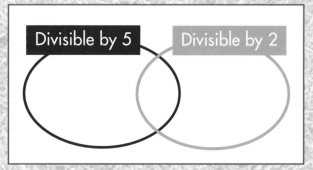

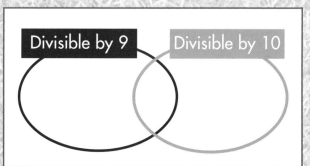

B Write true or false for each of these.

1 265 is divisible by 5 → _____

2 43 is divisible by 9 → _____

3 210 is divisible by 4 → _____

4 670 is divisible by 10 → _____

Arsenal FC v Atletico Madrid

GOALS

0	1
	2
	3
1	4
	5
	6
2	7
	8
	9
3	10
	11
4	12

Write whether these are true or false.

1 483 is divisible by 2 → _____

2 120 is divisible by 4 → _____

3 605 is divisible by 5 → _____

4 360 is divisible by 9 → _____

5 905 is divisible by 10 → _____

6 144 is divisible by 4 → _____

HALF-TIME

Use one, two or three of these digits. Arrange them to make two numbers that are divisible by:

3 **0** **6**

7	2	→	_____	_____
8	4	→	_____	_____
9	5	→	_____	_____
10	10	→	_____	_____
11	9	→	_____	_____
12	3	→	_____	_____

ARSENAL FC [ ]

ATLETICO MADRID **2**

Now turn to page 28 and fill in the score on the Super-League Results Table.

Total: [ ] **out of 12**

Colour the bar on the right to find out how many goals you've scored for Arsenal.

Block the Attacker!

A game for two players

You need:

3 counters of the same colour

1 counter of a different colour

How to play

- One player is the defender, with three counters, each starting on a D spot. The other player is the attacker, with a counter on the A spot.

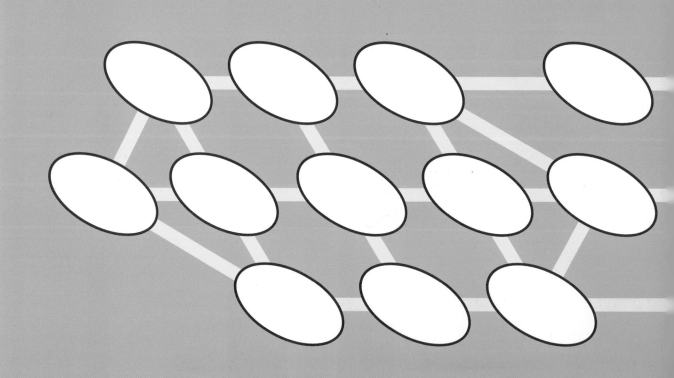

Aim: • The defenders trap the attacker so that the attacker can't move.

• The attacker moves the counter into the goal.

- The defender moves first and can only move one place to the left.
- The attacker can move one place in any direction.
- The players take turns to move.

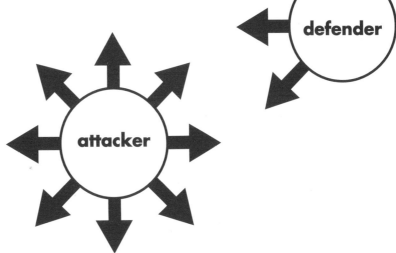

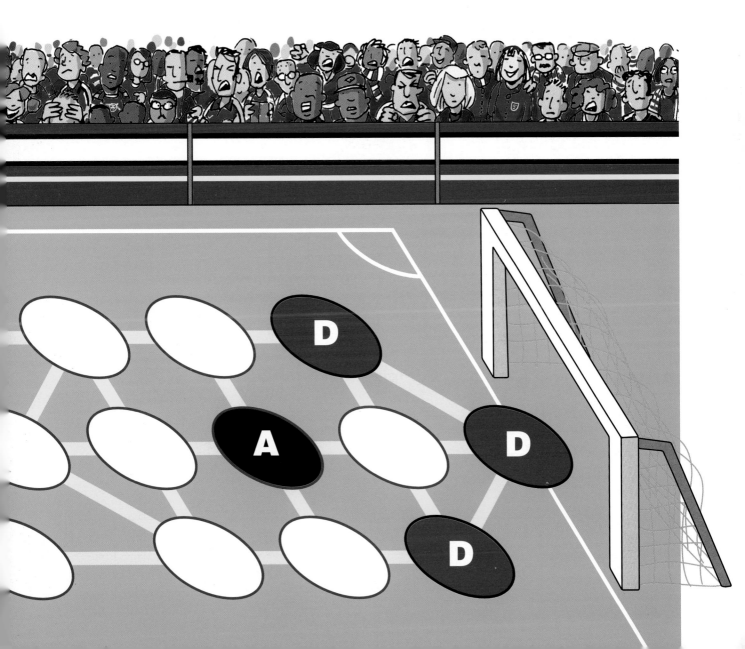

training

The decimal point separates units from tenths.

Tens	Units	•	Tenths	Hundredths
2	4	•	2	5
twenty	four	point	two	five

When you **multiply** a number by 10, the **digits** move one place to the **left**.

$$3.4 \times 10 = 34.0$$
$$17.2 \times 10 = 172.0$$
$$0.42 \times 10 = 4.20$$

When you **divide** a number by 10, the **digits** move one place to the **right**.

$$3.4 \div 10 = 0.34$$
$$17.2 \div 10 = 1.72$$
$$0.42 \div 10 = 0.042$$

practice

A Write the value of the red digit.

1 7.29 → 9 hundredths

2 13.74 →

3 43.82 →

4 8.06 →

5 13.61 →

6 19.8 →

B Look at these turnstiles. Complete each table.

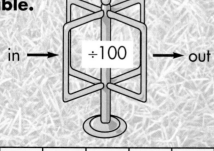

in → ×100 → out

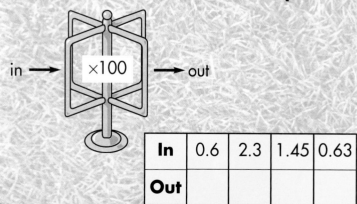

in → ÷100 → out

In	0.6	2.3	1.45	0.63
Out				

In	370	451	32	6
Out				

Arsenal FC v AS Roma

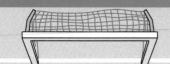

Write each of these using decimal numbers.

1 Three point one four → _____

2 Nine and three tenths → _____

3 Zero point eight two → _____

4 Six and four hundredths → _____

5 Nineteen and six tenths → _____

6 Four point zero four → _____

HALF-TIME

Multiply each number by 10.

7 4.3 → _____

8 6.15 → _____

9 0.05 → _____

Divide each number by 10.

10 15.6 → _____

11 1.7 → _____

12 26.9 → _____

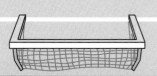

Total: [ ] **out of 12**

Colour the bar on the right to find out how many goals you've scored for Arsenal.

GOALS

0

1

2

3

4

1
2
3
4
5
6
7
8
9
10
11
12

ARSENAL FC [ ]

AS ROMA **2**

Now turn to page 28 and fill in the score on the Super-League Results Table.

The Strip

The patterns on many football clubs' shirts are based on symmetrical shapes. Two popular shapes are the square and the rectangle, on which the quartered shirt is based. However, Arsenal always preferred a large block of colour.

This shirt has one line of symmetry.

1 Design a symmetrical pattern on this shirt.

Some letters of the alphabet have line symmetry.

4 What are these words?

A mirror may help you to read them.

ᵃ D I C E

ᵇ B E E

ᶜ H I D E

ᵈ N A T

5 a Draw the lines of symmetry on the name of our star number 10.

b Which of these letters don't have symmetry? _____

Using symmetry in designs.

2 Draw the lines of symmetry.

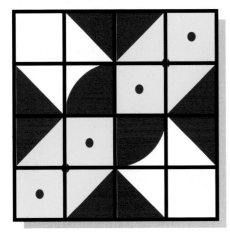

3 Now design symmetrical patterns on these grids.

Draw the lines of symmetry.

a 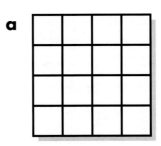 **b**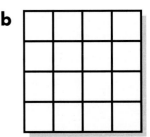

c 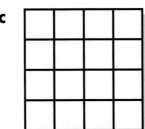 **d**

e   **f**

a _____

b _____

c _____

d _____

e _____

f _____

> **Did you know ... ?**
> In the very early days, the Arsenal goalkeeper wore a hand-knitted, woollen polo neck jumper. It must have been very hot!

DENNIS BERGKAMP

training

Per cent means **out of 100**. So, a percentage can be shown as a fraction of 100.

$$\frac{40}{100} = 40\%$$

$$\frac{25}{100} = 25\%$$

Common percentages

$$10\% = \frac{10}{100} = \frac{1}{10} = 0.1$$

$$25\% = \frac{25}{100} = \frac{1}{4} = 0.25$$

$$50\% = \frac{50}{100} = \frac{1}{2} = 0.5$$

1% of £1 = 1p

10% of £1 = 10p

20% of £1 = 20p

50% of £1 = 50p

% means per cent

practice

A Write the percentage shown in colour.

1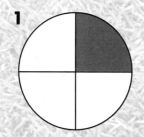

2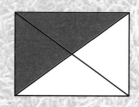

_____ %

3

_____ %

_____ %

B Write each of these as a percentage.

1 $\frac{3}{10}$ = [   ] %   **2** $\frac{65}{100}$ = [   ] %   **3** $\frac{7}{10}$ = [   ] %   **4** $\frac{95}{100}$ = [   ] %

C Answer these.

1

50% of	
£3 →	
£5 →	
£8 →	

2

20% of	
£2 →	
£12 →	
£15 →	

3

10% of	
£5 →	
£20 →	
£35 →	

Arsenal FC v Benfica

Write each percentage as a fraction.

1 40% →

2 5% →

3 25% →

4 70% →

5 30% →

6 75% →

HALF-TIME

Calculate each of these.

7 10% of £35 → _____

8 1% of £5 → _____

9 50% of £18 → _____

10 20% of £20 → _____

11 60% of £10 → _____

12 5% of £20 → _____

0	1
	2
	3
	4
1	5
	6
	7
2	8
	9
	10
3	11
4	12

ARSENAL FC

BENFICA **0**

Total: ☐ **out of 12**

Colour the bar on the right to find out how many goals you've scored for Arsenal.

Now turn to page 28 and fill in the score on the Super-League Results Table.

The Premier League

There are currently 20 teams in the FA Carling Premiership. Some cities have more than one team in this League.

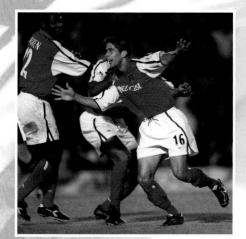

London   Arsenal, Charlton Athletic, Chelsea, Tottenham Hotspur, West Ham United.

Liverpool   Everton, Liverpool.

Manchester   Manchester City, Manchester United.

Aston Villa are based in **Birmingham**.

Travelling away.

This chart shows the distance in kilometres between some of the towns and cities with clubs in the Premier League. For example, the distance between London and Newcastle is 460 km.

Birmingham	Leeds	Liverpool	London	Manchester	Middlesbrough	Newcastle	Southampton
195							
163	119						
193	319	348					
144	71	56	328				
286	103	233	412	183			
335	150	280	460	232	63		
216	381	385	129	365	475	521	

Look at the map of England.

1 Name the other ten Premiership clubs in the 2000/2001 season.

_____

_____

_____

_____

_____

_____

_____

_____

_____

_____

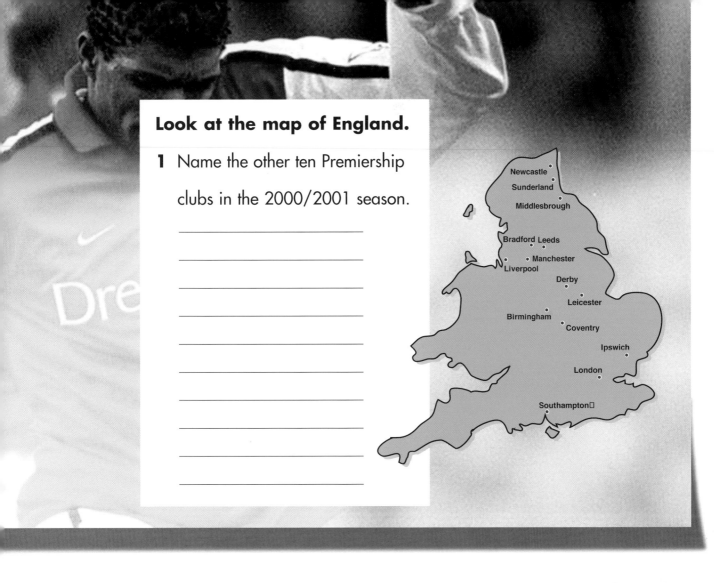

Newcastle
Sunderland
Middlesbrough
Bradford Leeds
Manchester
Liverpool
Derby
Leicester
Birmingham
Coventry
Ipswich
London
Southampton

Use the distance chart to answer these questions.

2 How far is it from London to ...

a Liverpool _____ km

b Southampton _____ km

c Birmingham _____ km

3 Which two cities are the furthest apart?

_____ and _____

4 Which two cities are the nearest to each other?

_____ and _____

5 How much further is it from Birmingham to Newcastle than from Birmingham to London? _____ km

6 What is the total distance of a journey from London to Leeds, and then from Leeds to Middlesbrough? _____ km

Pre-match Angles

training

90° is a **right** angle.

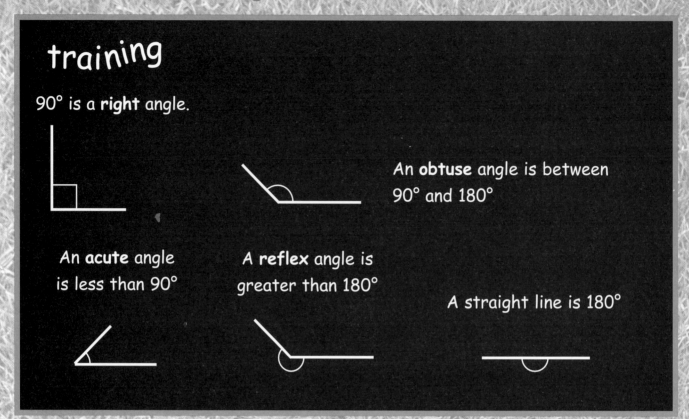

An **obtuse** angle is between 90° and 180°

An **acute** angle is less than 90°

A **reflex** angle is greater than 180°

A straight line is 180°

practice

A • Tick each acute angle in these shapes.

• Put a cross in each obtuse angle in these shapes.

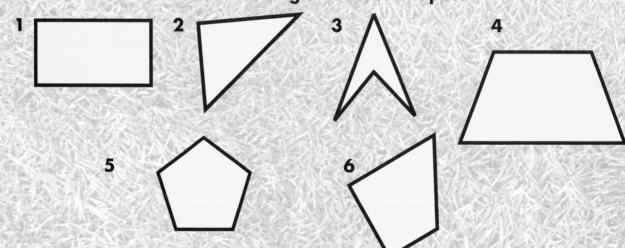

1   2   3   4

5   6

B Write the size of each missing angle.

1   120° [ ]°   2   70° [ ]°

3   30° [ ]°   4   90° [ ]°

Arsenal FC v Anderlecht

Tick each angle that is less than 90°.

1

2

3

4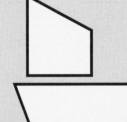

5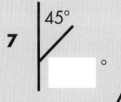

6

HALF-TIME

Write the size of each missing angle.

7 45°

[ ]°

8 130° [ ]°

9 [ ]°

125°

10 [ ]° 90°

11 160°

[ ]°

12 35°

[ ]°

Total: [ ] **out of 12**

Colour the bar on the right to find out how many goals you've scored for Arsenal.

GOALS

0	1
	2
	3
	4
1	5
	6
2	7
	8
	9
3	10
	11
4	12

ARSENAL FC [ ]

ANDERLECHT **1**

Now turn to page 28 and fill in the score on the Super-League Results Table.

Super-League Results

MATCH 1

Arsenal FC		Inter Milan	1
Anderlecht	2	Atl Madrid	1
St Etienne	0	Benfica	3

MATCH 2

Arsenal FC		St Etienne	1
Atl Madrid	2	Inter Milan	2
Anderlecht	1	AS Roma	3

MATCH 3

Atl Madrid	2	Arsenal FC	
St Etienne	2	Inter Milan	1
Benfica	1	AS Roma	3

MATCH 4

AS Roma	2	Arsenal FC	
Atl Madrid	1	St Etienne	2
Anderlecht	0	Benfica	0

MATCH 5

Benfica	0	Arsenal FC	
AS Roma	5	St Etienne	1
Anderlecht	0	Inter Milan	1

MATCH 6

Arsenal FC		Anderlecht	1
Inter Milan	2	Benfica	0
Atl Madrid	3	AS Roma	3

MATCH 7

AS Roma	2	Inter Milan	0
Atl Madrid	4	Benfica	1
Anderlecht	0	St Etienne	2

Super-League Tables

Enter the score for each match.

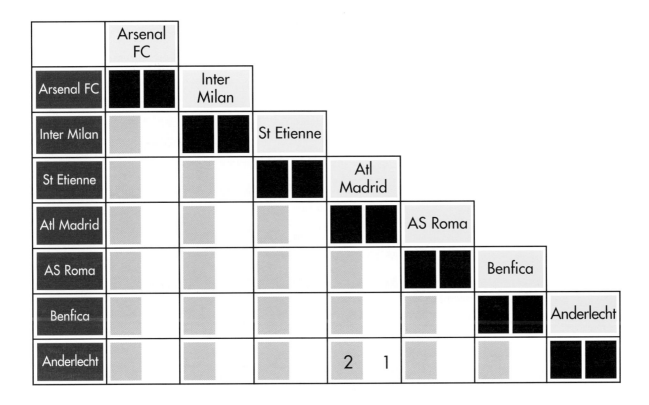

Complete the league table when all the matches are finished.

Win   3 pts   Draw   1 pt   Lose   0 pts

Team	Played	Won	Drew	Lost	For	Against	Goal diff	Points
Arsenal FC	6							
Inter Milan	6							
St Etienne	6							
Atl Madrid	6							
AS Roma	6							
Benfica	6							
Anderlecht	6							

Champions [   ]   Runners-up [   ]

The Stadium 4–5

1

Attendance	Date	Team
38 146	Oct 2000	Man United
38 014	Aug 2000	Liverpool
38 052	Dec 2000	Newcastle United
38 049	Oct 2000	Manchester City
38 042	Oct 2000	Aston Villa
38 036	Dec 2000	Southampton
38 025	Aug 2000	Charlton Athletic
37 794	Sept 2000	Coventry City
37 679	Nov 2000	Derby County

2 38 146 – 30 000 + 8000 + 100 + 40 + 6
37 679 – 30 000 + 7000 + 600 + 70 + 9
37 794 – 30 000 + 7000 + 700 + 90 + 4
38 014 – 30 000 + 8000 + 000 + 10 + 4

3 *There are many answers. Here is one example of ten (in order):*
9753
9723
9532
7925
7329
5732
3952
3295
2953
2753

Match 1 Data 6–7

Pre-match
1 9 **2** 7 **3** 146 cm **4** Rajesh
5 Ann and Dave **6** 36 cm **7** 6 **8** Jon and Rajesh

The Match
1 Game 8 **2** 4 **3** 1 **4** 7 **5** Game 12 **6** 26
7 0 and 2 **8** 5 **9** 0 **10** 3 **11** 2
12 0–0, 2–0 and 4–1

The 1970s 8–9
1 May 1971 **2** June 1974 **3** Charlie George
4 2 **5** European Fairs Cup **6** Check your timeline is accurate. **7** 31 **8** 31

Match 2 Area 10–11

Pre-match
A 1 Perimeter – 56 m Area – 160 m^2
2 Perimeter – 54 m Area – 144 m^2
3 Perimeter – 24 m Area – 27 m^2
B 1 64 cm^2 **2** 28 cm

The Match
1 6 cm^2 **2** 32 cm^2 **3** 63 cm^2 **4** 28 cm^2
5 24 cm^2 **6** 8 cm^2 **7** 22 cm **8** 22 cm
9 26 cm **10** 26 cm **11** 12 cm **12** 32 cm

The Arsenal FC Shop 12–13
1 a total £18.75, change £11.25;
b total £21.24, change £8.76;
c total £14.24, change £15.76
2 £17 **3** Yes **4** three mugs
5 Check the answer totals no more than £30
6a Three 35p stamps and two 25p stamps
b There are many different amounts

Match 3 Division 14–15

Pre-match
A 1

2

B 1 True **2** False **3** False **4** True

The Match
1 False **2** True **3** True **4** True **5** False
6 True
Any two of the following:
7 6 or 30 or 36 or 60 or 306 or 360 or 630
8 36 or 60 or 360 **9** 30 or 60 or 360 or 630
10 30 or 60 or 360 or 630
11 36 or 63 or 306 or 360 or 603 or 630
12 3 or 6 or 30 or 36 or 60 or 63 or 306 or 360 or 603 or 630

Match 4 Decimals 18–19

Pre-match
A 1 9 hundredths **2** 7 tenths **3** 3 units
4 6 hundredths **5** 6 tenths **6** 8 tenths
B 60   230   145   63
3.7   4.51   0.32   0.06

The Match
1 3.14 **2** 9.3 **3** 0.82 **4** 6.04 **5** 19.6
6 4.04 **7** 43 **8** 61.5 **9** 0.5 **10** 1.56
11 0.17 **12** 2.69

The Strip 20–21
1 Check the design is symmetrical
2

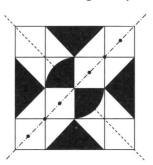

3 Check the lines of symmetry
4 a DICE **b** BEE **c** HIDE **d** MAT **e** MOUTH
 f TOOTH
5 a

DENNIS

BERGKAMP

b N R S G P

Match 5 Percentages 22–23

Pre-match
A 1 25% **2** 50% **3** 75%
B 1 30% **2** 65% **3** 70% **4** 95%
C 1 £1.50 £2.50 £4.00 **2** 40p £2.40 £3.00
 3 50p £2.00 £3.50

The Match

1 $\frac{40}{100}$ or $\frac{2}{5}$ **2** $\frac{5}{100}$ or $\frac{1}{20}$ **3** $\frac{25}{100}$ or $\frac{1}{4}$

4 $\frac{70}{100}$ or $\frac{7}{10}$ **5** $\frac{30}{100}$ or $\frac{3}{10}$ **6** $\frac{75}{100}$ or $\frac{3}{4}$

7 £3.50 **8** 5p **9** £9.00 **10** £4.00
11 £6.00 **12** £1.00

The Premier League 24–25
1 Newcastle United, Sunderland,
 Middlesbrough, Bradford City, Leeds United,
 Derby County, Leicester City, Coventry City,
 Ipswich Town and Southampton
2 a 348 km **b** 129 km **c** 193 km
3 Newcastle and Southampton
4 Liverpool and Manchester **5** 142 km
6 422 km

Match 6 Angles 26–27
Pre-match
A

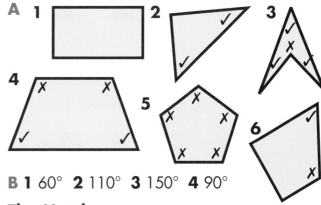

B 1 60° **2** 110° **3** 150° **4** 90°

The Match

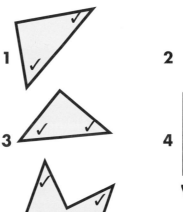
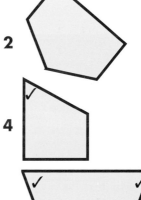

7 135° **8** 50° **9** 55° **10** 90° **11** 20°
12 145°

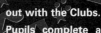

Collect the set

Each book introduces new skills and harder challenges.
Collect all 8 and be an English and Maths champion.

Arsenal FC English Books 1–4

Arsenal FC Maths Books 1–4

  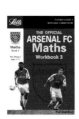 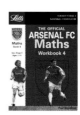

For all the latest news, views and information on

Arsenal FC

visit the official Arsenal website:

www.arsenal.com

Arsenal Football Club PLC
Arsenal Stadium, Highbury, London N5 1BU

Letts Educational, Aldine House, Aldine Place, London W12 8AW
Tel: 020 8740 2266 Fax: 020 8743 8451 E-mail: mail@lettsed.co.uk
Website: www.letts-education.com

Every effort has been made to trace copyright holders and obtain their permission for the use of copyright material. The authors and publishers will gladly receive information enabling them to rectify any error or omission in subsequent editions.

All facts are correct at time of going to press.

Published 2001
© Letts Educational Ltd
Author: Paul Broadbent
Editorial and Design: Moondisks Ltd, Cambridge
Illustrations: Joel Morris
Colour Reprographics: PDQ Digital Media Solutions Ltd, Bungay

Our thanks to the players and staff at Arsenal Football Club.
Photographs copyright Arsenal Football Club and Colorsport.

British Library Cataloguing in Publication Data
A CIP record for this book is available from the British Library.

ISBN 1-85805-889-9

Printed in the UK.

Letts Educational Limited is a member of Granada Learning Limited, part of the Granada Media Group.